Contents

The foxes go to town

"Berry! Billy! Bobby!" called Mrs Fox. "Come and sit down. We want to tell you something."

The three little foxes ran over to their mother and father.

"Now," said Mr Fox. "We're going to do something exciting. We're going to take you to the town."

"What's a town?" asked Berry.

"The town is a very funny place. It is where the animals with two legs live. They are called people," said Mrs Fox.

"Will we see these animals with two legs, Dad?" asked Billy.

"Yes. You'll see lots of the animals with two legs but you must all stay away from them. People mean danger for us."

"Why are we going to the town if it is so dangerous?" asked Bobby.

"We're going because the food there is so good," said Mrs Fox. "Yes, the food is the best in the world. Now come along. It's time to go."

The foxes went through the woods, over the bridge and along the road that went to the town.

"Dad, look. Lots of big buildings," said Berry.

"I know," said her father. "That's what the town is like."

"What are those small buildings?" asked Billy.

"That is where the animals with two legs live," said her mother. "They are called houses."

Suddenly, they heard a terrible noise.

"Quick! Into the grass!" shouted Mr Fox. The three little foxes were very frightened as they hid in the grass.

"Those were cars," said Mr Fox. "You must always keep away from cars. They are very dangerous. Now follow me and don't let any people see you."

They were very, very quiet. They walked into a garden and up the path.

5

"There," said Mrs Fox. "That is what we have come all this way for." There on the path sat three big dustbins.

"Oh, what a beautiful smell," said Berry.

"Oh, I like it as well," said Billy.

"That smell makes me feel very, very hungry," said Bobby.

6

"We need to tip over the dustbins," said Mr Fox.
"Then eat all you want. Run and hide if any people
come along. People don't like us taking food from
their dustbins."

"Why not?" said Berry.

"I don't know," said her mother. "Funny animals,
people. They don't want to eat it, that I do know."

"Are you sure?" said Berry. "It smells so good."

"I'm sure," said Mrs Fox. "Now, we need to push this
dustbin over. One, two, three, go!"

The three little foxes helped to push the dustbin.
It went over with a bang.

"Now eat," shouted Mr Fox. And they did. They ate and ate and ate.

"I'll have to stop," said Berry.

"I can't go on," said Billy.

"Nor can I," said Bobby.

"Now let's all go and sleep," said Mr Fox. "After all that food, it's a lovely thing to do. Come on, you three, hide and go to sleep."

When they woke up again, they saw a girl and a boy by the dustbins. The foxes kept very quiet and still.

"Oh, look," said the girl. "What a disgusting mess!"

"That smell is just terrible," said the boy.

"We'd better clear it up," said the girl. "How disgusting."

"How funny," thought Mrs Fox. "To the children it smells disgusting, but to us it's the best smell in the world."

When the children had gone and the street was quiet,
the foxes went back home.

"Well, children, did you have fun today?" asked
Mr Fox.

"Oh, yes," cried the little foxes. "We had a lovely
time and we ate the best food in the world!"

The fox

Some people, such as postmen and milkmen, have to get up very early in the morning. Sometimes, as they are going along a quiet road, they might see something that looks like a small brown dog with pointed ears and a white tip to its tail. But it is not a lost dog looking for a home. It is a hungry fox looking for food.

Some foxes look for food in dustbins.

Foxes eat lots of different kinds of food. They like to
eat mice and rabbits best, but they also feed on other
small animals and even caterpillars. In the autumn they
find blackberries and apples. Many foxes now live in
towns and get food from dustbins and rubbish tips.

Foxes live in burrows or dig a hole in the ground.
This is called a den. In the spring, the mother fox makes
a special place for the baby foxes in a hole or in a quiet
place under an old shed. The baby foxes are called cubs.

Fox cubs like playing.

At first, the mother fox stays with the cubs and looks
after them all the time and their father brings food for
her. When the cubs are about four weeks old, they are
big and strong enough to go out and play. They like to
fight and chase and play tug-of-war.

14

The badger

Badgers have a black and white face and a grey back.
They have four legs with strong claws for digging.
They have small eyes and they can't see very well, but
they have very good ears.

Badgers live in woods and under hedges. You don't
see them very often because they sleep in the day and
only come out at night.

Badgers change their bedding when it gets dirty.

Badgers live in a hole under the ground called a sett. They make a sett by digging lots of long tunnels. At the end of these tunnels, there are special holes where the badgers sleep. They make a bed with grass, leaves and plants. Badgers are very clean animals and they take the old bed out when it gets dirty and make a new one. Badgers live in the same sett for years and years.

Badgers like to live as a family in their sett. There is a mother, a father and two or three baby badgers. Sometimes another family lives with them. All the badgers sleep in the same bed to keep warm. They clean each other's fur.

Baby badgers like to play. They roll and jump over each other or try to catch each other, running in and out of the tunnels.

At night, badgers come out of the sett to look for food. They always walk along the same path so sometimes you can see their paw prints in the mud or bits of fur stuck on a fence.

Badgers like all sorts of food so they have no trouble finding enough to eat. They catch animals such as worms, beetles, rabbits and hedgehogs. They also like eating plants such as grass, berries and nuts.

The hedgehog

In the daytime, hedgehogs sleep under a hedge or even under a garden shed. They make nests from leaves and grass. Hedgehogs like to live alone. At night, they go to look for food. They catch beetles, caterpillars and worms.

Hedgehogs curl up when there is danger.

Some people like to feed hedgehogs in their garden. Bread and milk can be bad for hedgehogs so it's best to give them a tin of dog or cat food.

A hedgehog has fur on its face and tummy but it has prickles all over its back. There can be as many as seven thousand prickles and they help to keep the hedgehog from danger. When a hedgehog is frightened, it rolls up into a ball. Only badgers or foxes are strong enough to hurt a hedgehog through its prickles.

Baby hedgehogs are blind at first.

At first, baby hedgehogs can't see or hear. They have soft, white prickles on their backs. After about two days, they get another set of hard brown prickles. The mother feeds the baby hedgehogs with her milk until they are old enough to find their own food. She looks after them and keeps them away from danger by carrying them in her mouth.

Hedgehogs can walk a long way when they are looking for food. They can run very fast, even though they have short legs. They can also get over a fence or swim across a river.

Roads are a big problem for hedgehogs. It is very hard for them to cross the road safely. When a car comes along, a hedgehog is frightened by the bright lights and it rolls into a ball or just stays still. Many hedgehogs die because they are run over by cars or lorries.

Nettles

Adam and Susie were playing football in the garden. Adam wanted to try out the new football gloves that he had got for his birthday.

"Your new gloves can't stop me!" laughed Susie, as the football whizzed past Adam.

"Oh no!" cried Adam. "Look at the football! It's gone into the nettles!"

Adam and Susie went to find the football which was stuck in the nettles. It was hard to get it because the nettles were tall and they didn't want to get stung.

"Mum wants to cut these nettles down," said Susie.

"I wish she would," said Adam. "I've just been stung on my legs." He pulled at one of the nettles, with his hands safely inside his gloves. Then he stopped suddenly.

"What's this?" he asked in surprise.

Susie came and looked. There were lots of big black caterpillars on the nettles. They had short prickles on their backs and they were eating the leaves.

"Don't they get stung?" asked Adam.

"No," said Susie. "These caterpillars only eat nettles. They don't like any other food. We kept some at school once and they turned into beautiful peacock butterflies."

"Look under this leaf," said Adam. He pointed to something. "Look. Little white eggs. What a funny place to put your eggs!"

"Not at all," said Susie. "When the eggs turn into caterpillars, they don't have to go and look for food because they are sitting on it! Let's see if any other animals live in the nettles, too."

"They wouldn't be so silly," laughed Adam.

Adam didn't think they would find any more animals, but he helped Susie to look. He was very surprised to see a grasshopper sitting on a leaf. He tried to catch it but it jumped away. Then a beetle ran quickly into a hole in the earth under the nettles.

"Look at this clever spider," said Susie. "It's building a web."

"Can you get your football?" called Mum. "Those nettles are a problem. I've got my shears here. I'll come and cut them down."

"No!" shouted Adam.

"We won't have any peacock butterflies," said Susie.

"And the grasshopper and the beetle will have to find a new home," said Adam. "And the spider will have to make a new web, too."

Mum smiled. "I didn't know you liked the nettles so much!" she said. "Shall we have some for tea? People ate them in the past."

"Oh, no!" said Adam.

"I think I would like chips better!" said Susie.

Life in the hedge

A hedge sometimes looks empty, like a long fence of green leaves. Look again and there are sure to be many surprises. There are all sorts of wild animals living in a hedge. Birds hide their nests safely in the trees. Rabbits dig burrows in the ground under the hedge. Hedgehogs like to sleep through the day in the leaves there.

Many animals come to the hedge to find food. A wild hedge is filled with lots of different plants. Badgers like to eat the berries and caterpillars eat the leaves. You might even see a squirrel looking for nuts or a mouse eating seeds.

Some animals come to the hedge to look for the smaller animals that live there. They want to eat them. A hungry fox looks for rabbits and many birds try to catch mice.

A hedge is not always such a lovely home. Sometimes people throw their rubbish into the hedge. Old bottles and tins can be a danger to wild animals. A mouse can get stuck in a bottle and it will soon die without food. Badgers and rabbits might get cut on broken bottles.

Sometimes people cut down hedges to make space for new houses and big roads. This is a big problem for the animals living in the hedge. Suddenly they lose their homes and their food. Some animals can live anywhere, but some animals can't. Some caterpillars will only eat one or two sorts of plants. Badgers like to live well away from people. Where can the animals go if their hedge is cut down?